I  COLOURING CHRISTMAS

Buster Books

Illustrated by
Hannah Davies, Beth Gunnell,
Ann Kronheimer, Sally Moret,
Emily Parker, Jay Raine,
Jeannine Rundle, Nellie Ryan
and Greg Stevenson

Edited by
Philippa Wingate

Designed by
Zoe Bradley

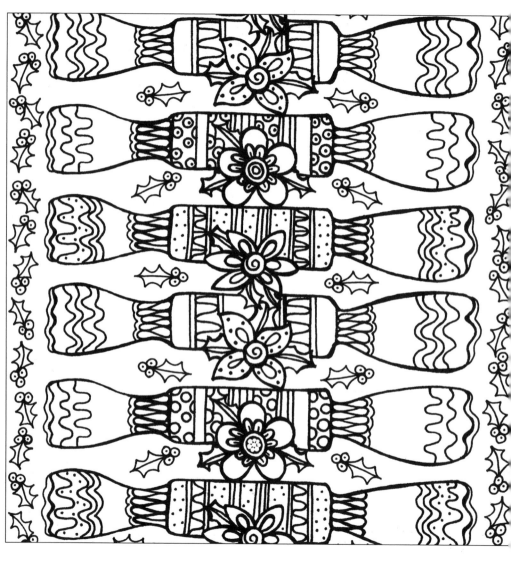

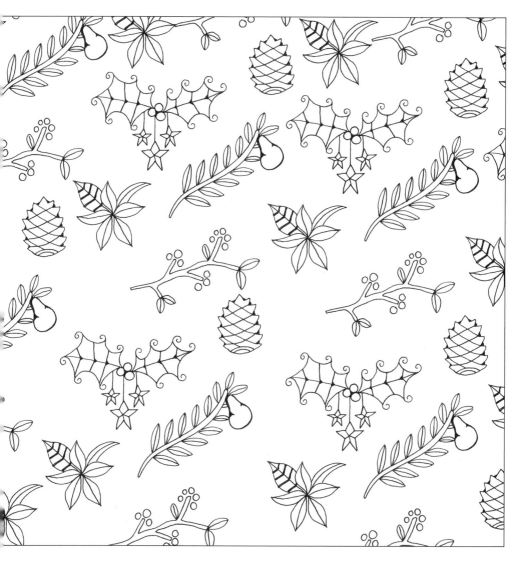

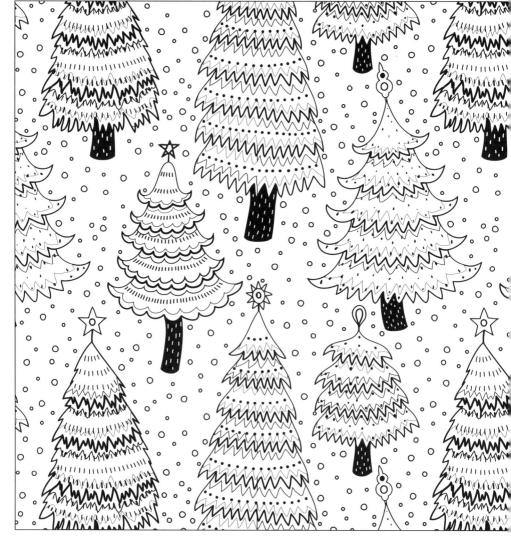

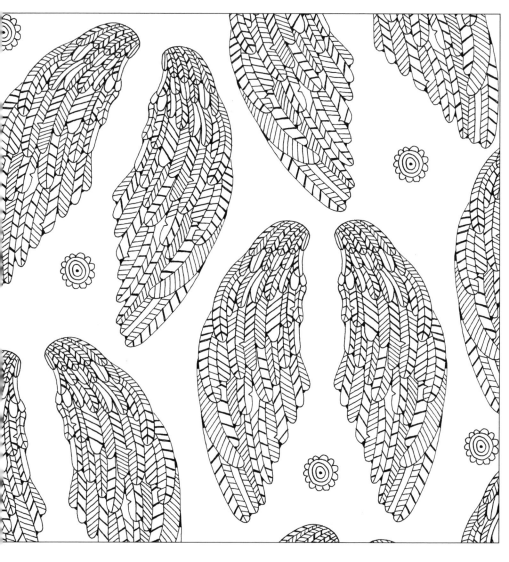

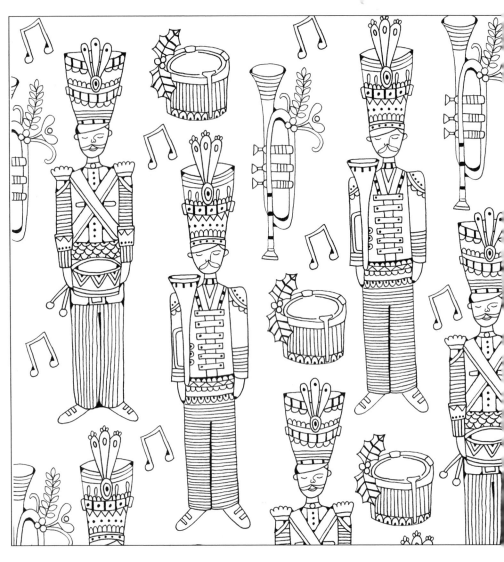

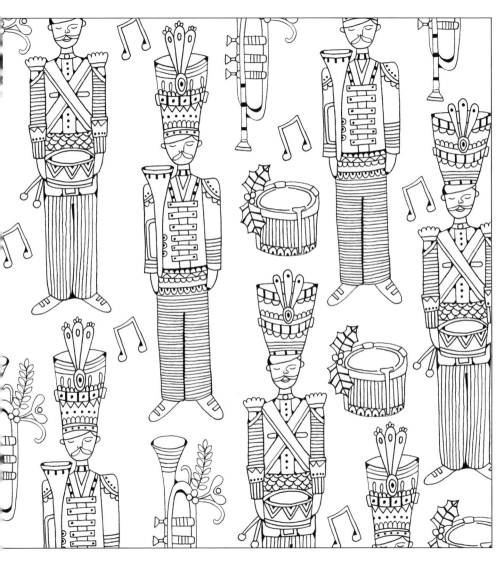